STRENGTH BECOMES YOU

TEEN JOURNAL

A GUIDED PATH TO SELF CONFIDENCE, CONSCIOUS THINKING & SELF WORTH

KATHLEEN QUINTON

COPYRIGHTED MATERIAL

Copyright © 2022 by Kathleen Quinton
All rights reserved.

All rights reserved. No part of Strength Becomes You Teen Journal may be reproduced, distributed, or transmitted in any form or by any means, including photocopying, recording, or other electronic or mechanical methods including information storage and retrieval systems, without prior permission in writing from the author except in the case of brief quotations embodied in critical reviews and certain other noncommercial uses permitted by copyright law.

Although the author has made every effort to ensure that the information in this book was correct at press time, the author does not assume and hereby disclaims any liability to any party for any loss, damage, or disruption caused by errors or omissions, whether such errors or omissions result from negligence, accident, or any other cause.

Adherence to all applicable laws and regulations, including international, federal, state and local governing professional licensing, business practices, advertising, and all other aspects of doing business in the US, Canada, or any other jurisdiction is the sole responsibility of the reader and consumer.

The author assumes no responsibility or liability whatsoever on behalf of the consumer or reader of this material. Any perceived slight of any individual or organization is purely unintentional.

The resources in this book are provided for informational purposes only and should not be used to replace the specialized training and professional judgment of a health care or mental health care professional.

The author cannot be held responsible for the use of the information provided within this book. Please always consult a trained professional before making any decision regarding treatment of yourself or others.

This is a work of creative nonfiction. Some parts have been fictionalized in varying degrees, for various purposes. Names, characters, places, and incidents either are products of the authors imagination or are used fictitiously. Any resemblance to actual persons, living or dead, events, or locales is entirely coincidental.

ISBN# 978-1-7337067-8-0

Kathleen Quinton
Visit my website at www.quintessential-coaching.com

Teen Advisor: Emma Morrissey
Editor: Lisa Tynan
Graphic Design: Antonia Boulton

Quintessential Productions
Marlborough, Massachusetts, USA
First paperback edition 2022

COPYRIGHTED MATERIAL

This Journal is inspired by those who
bravely come forward to share their
own special brand of magic.
Thank you for making the world
a better place

COPYRIGHTED MATERIAL

YOUR ARE A STAR

COPYRIGHTED MATERIAL

THIS JOURNAL BELONGS TO:

____

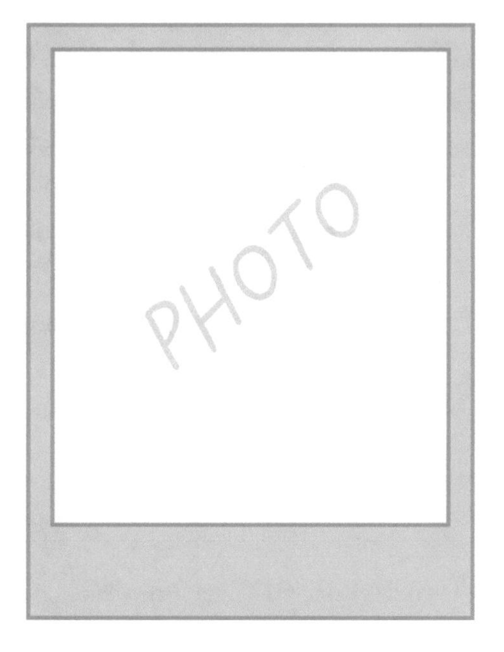

STARTING DATE:

MONTH:........................

YEAR:...........................

AGE:.............................

COPYRIGHTED MATERIAL

"Our deepest fear is not that we are inadequate. Our deepest fear is that we are powerful beyond measure. It is our light, not our darkness that most frightens us. We ask ourselves, 'Who am I to be brilliant, gorgeous, talented, fabulous?' Actually, who are you not to be?"

~Marianne Williamson

COPYRIGHTED MATERIAL

INTRODUCTION

WELCOME TO YOUR STRENGTH BECOMES YOU TEEN JOURNAL

YOUR POTENTIAL IS LIMITLESS!

THIS JOURNAL IS A SACRED PLACE TO HOLD YOUR THOUGHTS AND DREAMS. A PLACE WHERE YOU CAN CONFIRM TO YOURSELF THAT YOUR VALUE AND YOUR ABILITY TO ACCOMPLISH GOALS IS REAL.

INSIDE YOU WILL FIND SELF-DISCOVERY PROMPTS TO HELP YOU TO UNCOVER AND BUILD UPON YOUR INNER STRENGTHS -

STRENGTHS THAT YOU ALREADY HAVE BUT MAY NOT HAVE REALISED YET, BUT YOU DO HAVE THEM!

YOU MAY ALSO DISCOVER....

WHAT DO YOU BELIEVE?

WHAT IS IT THAT YOU WANT? WHAT MAKES YOU HAPPY ?

WHAT ARE YOUR DREAMS?

WHAT WORRIES YOU? AND......WHAT YOU CAN DO ABOUT IT!?

THIS JOURNAL WAS CREATED FOR YOU TO LEARN MORE ABOUT YOURSELF AND HOW TO BETTER NAVIGATE THIS WORLD YOU LIVE IN!

SELF-DISCOVERY CAN BE A CHALLENGING YET EXCITING ADVENTURE. ONE THING WE KNOW FOR SURE IT IS.........

ALWAYS, ALWAYS, ALWAYS A REWARDING JOURNEY!

CHEERS TO A FANTASTIC YEAR OF SELF-DISCOVERY

ALL MY VERY BEST,

Kathy

COPYRIGHTED MATERIAL

TIPS FOR USING THE 12 MONTH 'STRENGTH BECOMES YOU ~ TEEN JOURNAL'

- FILL IN THE 'THIS JOURNAL BELONGS TO YOU' PAGE. FILL IN YOUR NAME, ADD YOUR PHOTO OR A FAVORITE PHOTO THAT RESONATES WITH YOU. FILL IN STARTING DATE & YEAR.
- FILL IN THE 'I AM' PAGES WITH YOUR NAME OR EVEN HOW YOU FEEL. FOR EXAMPLE, "I AM JULIA", "I AM CARLOS" OR "I AM HAPPY/SAD/EXCITED/BRILLIANT", WHATEVER YOU CHOOSE
- NOTE THE WRITING PROMPTS THROUGHOUT THE JOURNAL. FOR INSTANCE: 'WHO AM I? WHAT MAKES MY HEART SING? WHAT ARE MY STRENGTHS & GIFTS? WHAT MAKES ME FEEL SUCCESSFUL? WHAT CAN I ACCOMPLISH?

  TIP: NOTICE IF YOUR ANSWERS & THOUGHTS CHANGE THROUGHOUT THE YEAR.
- EACH MONTH THINK ABOUT WHAT YOU WANT & WHAT YOUR PRIORITIES ARE. SET GOALS & CREATE ACTION STEPS.

  TIP: ACCOMPLISHING GOALS BECOMES MORE MANAGEABLE WHEN WE ARE GOING AFTER WHAT WE WANT!
- THERE ARE PLENTY OF FREE WRITING PAGES TO DREAM YOUR BIGGEST DREAMS, SOLVE PROBLEMS & BE YOUR CREATIVE SELF.

  TIP: YOUR THOUGHTS & DREAMS ARE SIGNIFICANT!
- HAVE FUN WITH THE WORD SEARCHES. WRITE WHAT INSPIRES YOU ABOUT THE FIRST FOUR WORDS THAT YOU FIND. WHAT DO THEY MEAN TO YOU? I WONDER WHY YOU SAW THOSE WORDS FIRST.
- THE REVIEW PAGE IS WHERE YOU WILL RECAP THE PREVIOUS MONTH'S HAPPENINGS. DID YOU ACCOMPLISH ONE OF YOUR GOALS? ARE YOU CLOSE? DID A NEW PRIORITY SHOW UP? HOW'S SCHOOL? HOW ARE YOU FEELING? HOW ARE YOUR FRIENDS? FAMILY? WHAT DID YOU LEARN? AND MORE.

  TIP: THINKING ABOUT WHAT IS HAPPENING AROUND YOU & FOR YOU IS EMPOWERING. BEING AWARE IS A SUPERPOWER!
- CLOSING THE MONTH IS THE CELEBRATION PAGE, AN ESSENTIAL STEP TO REINFORCE YOUR ACCOMPLISHMENTS. BIG OR SMALL, CELEBRATE THEM ALL! PAT YOURSELF ON THE BACK OR DO A HAPPY DANCE! YOUR STRENGTHS & GIFTS SHOULD BE (ACKNOWLEDGED BY YOU) & CELEBRATED.

  TIP: THEY MAY VERY WELL BE YOUR SUPERPOWERS. THESE STRENGTHS HELP YOU BECOME YOU ~ & THERE IS ONLY ONE YOU!

COPYRIGHTED MATERIAL

I AM .... , AND THIS IS MY JOURNAL: MY PLACE TO HOLD MY INNERMOST THOUGHTS AND FEELINGS, ACCOMPLISHMENTS AND CHALLENGES, DREAMS AND FEARS, JOYS AND HEARTACHES, AND COUNTLESS OTHER LIFE MOMENTS TO CHERISH AND CELEBRATE.

AS I JOURNAL, I WILL LEARN MORE ABOUT MYSELF AND WHAT I WANT, I WILL DISCOVER MY STRENGTHS AND GIFTS. I WILL MAKE UP MY MIND, AND SOMETIMES I WILL CHANGE MY MIND. I WILL WRITE MY THOUGHTS FOR TODAY AND UNDERSTAND THAT TOMORROW THEY MAY CHANGE. I WILL BE A CONSCIOUS THINKER AND REMAIN OPENMINDED. I WILL SORT THINGS OUT AND BE INSPIRED. I WILL KEEP GROWING AND MOVING FORWARD. I WILL FIND MY SPARK AND OWN IT. I WILL FIGURE OUT WHAT MAKES ME HAPPY, STRONG, SUCCESSFUL, AND WELL, ME!

COPYRIGHTED MATERIAL

KNOWING WHAT I WANT =

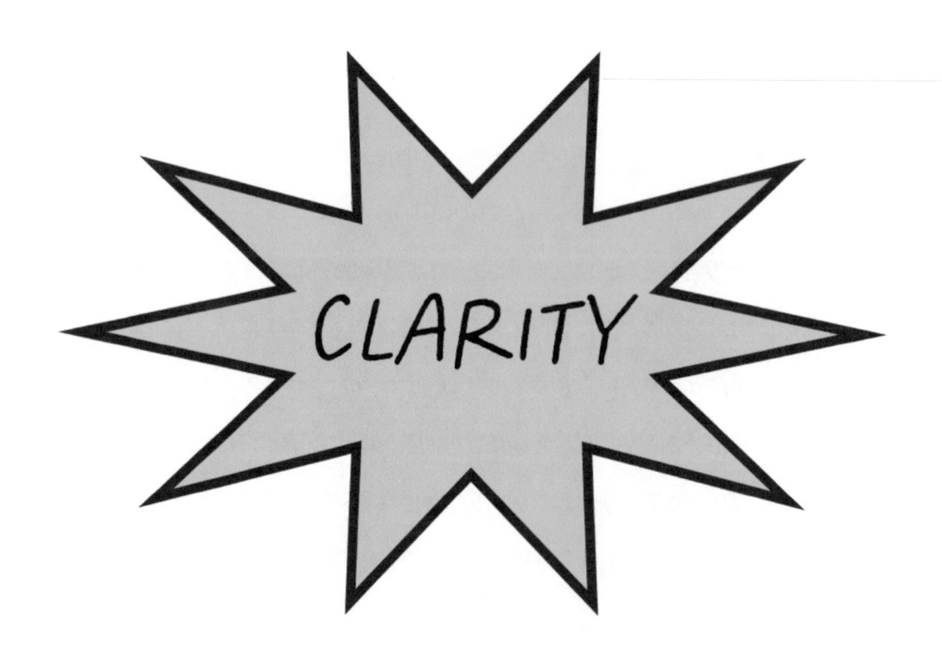

COPYRIGHTED MATERIAL

MONTH 1 STARTING DATE: ....

CONSCIOUSLY KNOWING WHAT I WANT BRINGS CLARITY. SO THAT'S A GOOD THING. IF I KNOW WHAT I WANT AND HAVE CONVICTION ABOUT IT, IT BECOMES EASIER TO SET GOALS AND FIGURE OUT HOW TO ACCOMPLISH THEM!

Take some time to think about the following questions & jot down any ideas that come to mind......

What are my gifts/strengths?
Who am I?
What makes my heart sing?
What can I accomplish?
ME
What makes me feel successful?

COPYRIGHTED MATERIAL

WHAT DO I WANT?

PERHAPS.......

ITS GOOD TO KNOW WHAT I WANT! HAVING CLARITY GIVES ME DIRECTION, FOCUS AND THE JOY OF KNOWING HOW TO ACCOMPLISH MY GOALS.

COPYRIGHTED MATERIAL

YOU'LL SET THOUSANDS OF GOALS IN YOUR LIFETIME, BUT FOR TODAY, LET'S START WITH 1-3 CONSCIOUSLY CHOSEN HIGH PRIORITY GOALS. SETTING ONE GOAL A MONTH IS GOOD ENOUGH. IN FACT, IT'S BETTER THAN GOOD ENOUGH. THERE ARE SHORT TERM GOALS LIKE STUDYING AN HOUR EACH NIGHT, IN ADDITION TO LONG TERM GOALS, LIKE SAVING MONEY TO BUY A CAR. THERE'S A LOT OF POWER IN SETTING A GOAL.

GOAL SETTING = POWER

MY GOALS THIS MONTH

1. I want to be healthier ☑
2. I want to be an includer ☑
3. I want to be creative ☑

ACTION STEPS

THERE IS POWER & ENERGY THAT COMES TO YOU WHEN YOU TAKE JUST ONE POSITIVE STRATEGIC ACTION STEP! CAN YOU IMAGINE IF YOU TAKE FIVE!

GOAL I want to be healthier

1. Eat more vegetables ☑
2. Smile more ☑
3. Be thankful ☑
4. Go to bed earlier ☑
5. Exercise at least 3-5 times a week ☑

COPYRIGHTED MATERIAL

GOAL SETTING

YOU'LL SET THOUSANDS OF GOALS IN YOUR LIFETIME, BUT FOR TODAY, LET'S START WITH 1-3 CONSCIOUSLY CHOSEN HIGH PRIORITY GOALS. SETTING ONE GOAL A MONTH IS GOOD ENOUGH. IN FACT, IT'S BETTER THAN GOOD ENOUGH. THERE ARE SHORT TERM GOALS LIKE STUDYING AN HOUR EACH NIGHT, IN ADDITION TO LONG TERM GOALS, LIKE SAVING MONEY TO BUY A CAR. THERE'S A LOT OF POWER IN SETTING A GOAL.

GOAL SETTING = POWER

MY GOALS THIS MONTH

1. .... ☐

2. .... ☐

3. .... ☐

ACTION STEPS

THERE IS POWER & ENERGY THAT COMES TO YOU WHEN YOU TAKE JUST ONE POSITIVE STRATEGIC ACTION STEP! CAN YOU IMAGINE IF YOU TAKE FIVE!

GOAL ....

1. .... ☐

2. .... ☐

3. .... ☐

4. .... ☐

5. .... ☐

COPYRIGHTED MATERIAL

MY THOUGHTS & DREAMS

COPYRIGHTED MATERIAL

I CAN............

COPYRIGHTED MATERIAL

JOURNAL PAGE

I WILL............

COPYRIGHTED MATERIAL

COPYRIGHTED MATERIAL

I BELIEVE............

JOURNAL PAGE

COPYRIGHTED MATERIAL

COPYRIGHTED MATERIAL

I REALISE.............

JOURNAL PAGE

COPYRIGHTED MATERIAL

DOODLE AWAY!

COPYRIGHTED MATERIAL

MONTHLY REVIEW

I'M PROUD OF MYSELF TODAY BECAUSE:

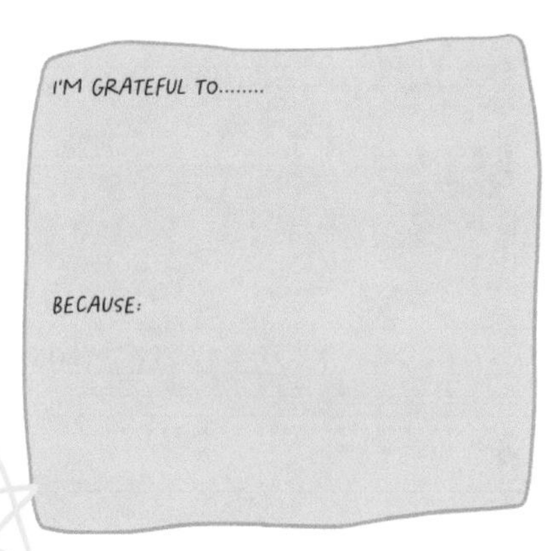

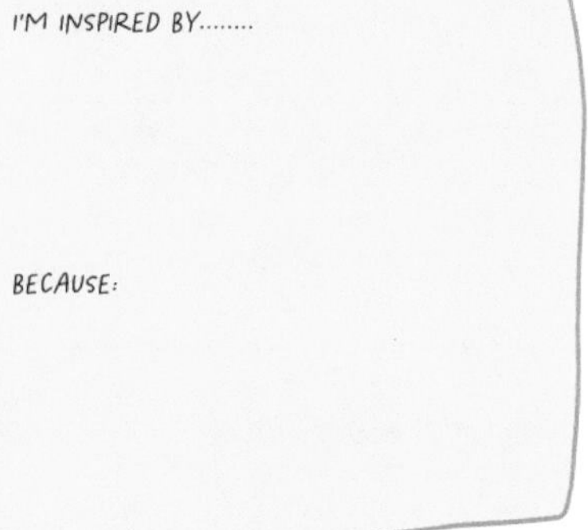

I USE MY MISTAKES AS THE LESSONS THEY ARE MEANT TO BE! THE MOST SUCCESSFUL PEOPLE IN THE WORLD MAKE MISTAKES TOO. THEY DON'T LIKE MAKING MISTAKES EITHER, BUT THEY DON'T DWELL ON THEM. THEY LEARN FROM THEM, AND DO A QUICK TURNAROUND.

COPYRIGHTED MATERIAL

END OF MONTH CELEBRATION!

WHAT WAS FUN?

WHAT DID I CHANGE?

WHAT WAS HARD?

WHAT DID I LEARN?

WHAT MADE ME LAUGH?

HOW DID I GROW?

WHO DID I INCLUDE?

WHAT DID I ACCOMPLISH?

HOW DID I PLOW THROUGH THE HARD STUFF?

COPYRIGHTED MATERIAL

MONTH 2 STARTING DATE: ....

MY NAME IS.. AND I BELIEVE IN MYSELF AND MY ABILITIES.

I AM SMART, STRONG AND EMPATHETIC. I VALUE MY FAMILY AND FRIENDS. I HAVE VALUE TOO. I LIKE TO PURSUE MY INTERESTS. I LIKE TO GET AND GIVE COMPLIMENTS.

I LIKE TO HAVE FUN AND BE AROUND FUN-LOVING PEOPLE. I KEEP MY SAFETY IN MIND AS I PURSUE MY DREAMS. I AM TENACIOUS IN A GOOD AND HUMBLE WAY.

Think about what you want to accomplish, have happen, and how you want to feel. What is most important to you & will benefit you now and grow with you?

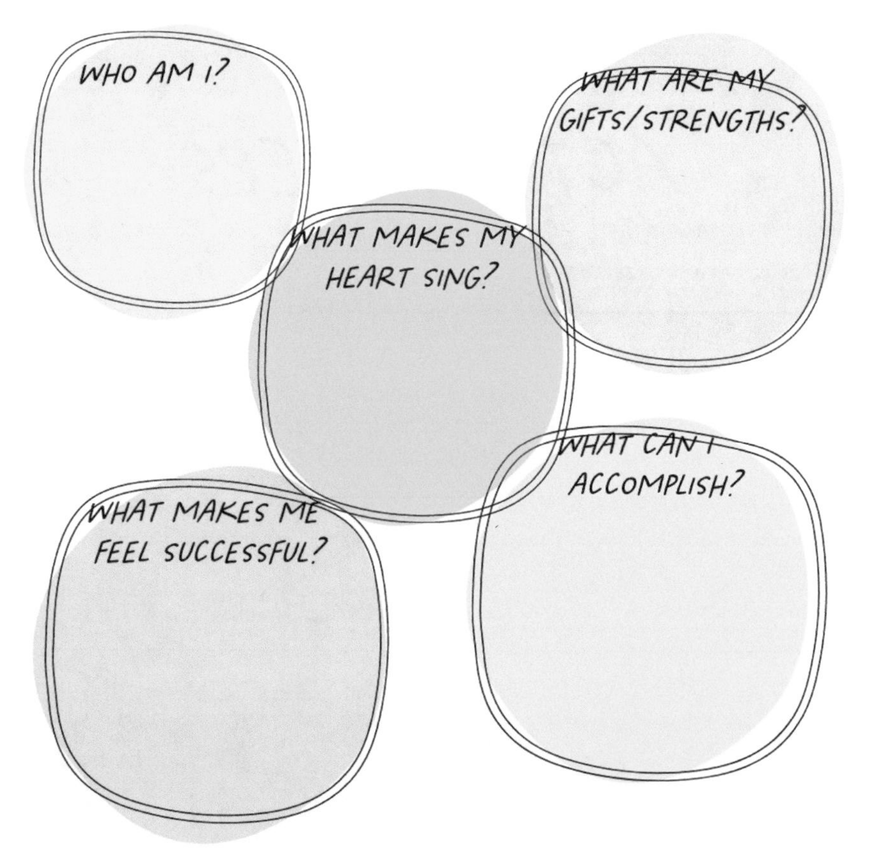
WHO AM I?
WHAT ARE MY GIFTS/STRENGTHS?
WHAT MAKES MY HEART SING?
WHAT CAN I ACCOMPLISH?
WHAT MAKES ME FEEL SUCCESSFUL?

COPYRIGHTED MATERIAL

GOAL SETTING

WHAT I WANT: LIST 1-3 THINGS. YOU CAN DUPLICATE PAST WANTS/GOALS AND MANY TIMES YOU'LL WANT TO! REMEMBER, SETTING EVEN ONE GOAL PER MONTH IS MORE THAN GOOD ENOUGH!

GOAL SETTING
=
POWER

MY GOALS THIS MONTH

1. ....

2. ....

3. ....

ACTION STEPS

ACTIONS I'LL TAKE: CREATE 1-5 ACTION STEPS PER GOAL THAT YOU CAN TAKE TO ACCOMPLISH YOUR OBJECTIVE.

GOAL ....

1. ....

2. ....

3. ....

4. ....

5. ....

COPYRIGHTED MATERIAL

MY THOUGHTS & DREAMS

COPYRIGHTED MATERIAL

JOURNAL PAGE

I THINK............

COPYRIGHTED MATERIAL

COPYRIGHTED MATERIAL

I LOVE.............

COPYRIGHTED MATERIAL

COPYRIGHTED MATERIAL

I THANK...........

COPYRIGHTED MATERIAL

COPYRIGHTED MATERIAL

I ENJOY............

COPYRIGHTED MATERIAL

DOODLE AWAY!

COPYRIGHTED MATERIAL

MORE DOODLING !

COPYRIGHTED MATERIAL

MONTHLY REVIEW

I'M PROUD OF MYSELF TODAY BECAUSE:

I'M GRATEFUL TO........

BECAUSE:

I'M INSPIRED BY........

BECAUSE:

I KNOW THAT I CAN, I WILL, AND I DO MAKE A DIFFERENCE! THAT'S HOW I THINK. I FEEL AN ENERGY INSIDE OF MYSELF PULLING ME TO LEARN MORE AND DO MORE. I WILL TAKE THE STEPS TO MAKE MY DREAMS A REALITY.

THE LUCKIER I FEEL THE LUCKIER I BECOME!

(FUNNY HOW THAT WORKS!)

COPYRIGHTED MATERIAL

END OF MONTH CELEBRATION!

WHAT WAS FUN?

WHAT WAS HARD?

WHAT MADE ME LAUGH?

WHO DID I INCLUDE?

WHAT DID I CHANGE?

WHAT DID I LEARN?

HOW DID I GROW?

WHAT DID I ACCOMPLISH?

HOW DID I PLOW THROUGH THE HARD STUFF?

COPYRIGHTED MATERIAL

MONTH 3 STARTING DATE: ....

I AM ...., AND I AM MORE POWERFUL THAN I KNEW! I CAN SET AND ACCOMPLISH GOALS AND HAVE FUN DOING IT. KINDNESS, LAUGHTER, AND TEAMWORK ARE STRENGTHS OF MINE! I HAVE GREAT INSTINCTS, AND I PAY CLOSE ATTENTION TO THEM. MY INSTINCTS HELP ME TO SET CLEAR BOUNDARIES FOR MYSELF AND KEEP ME SAFE.

Think about what you want to accomplish, have happen, and how you want to feel. What is most important to you & will benefit you now and grow with you?

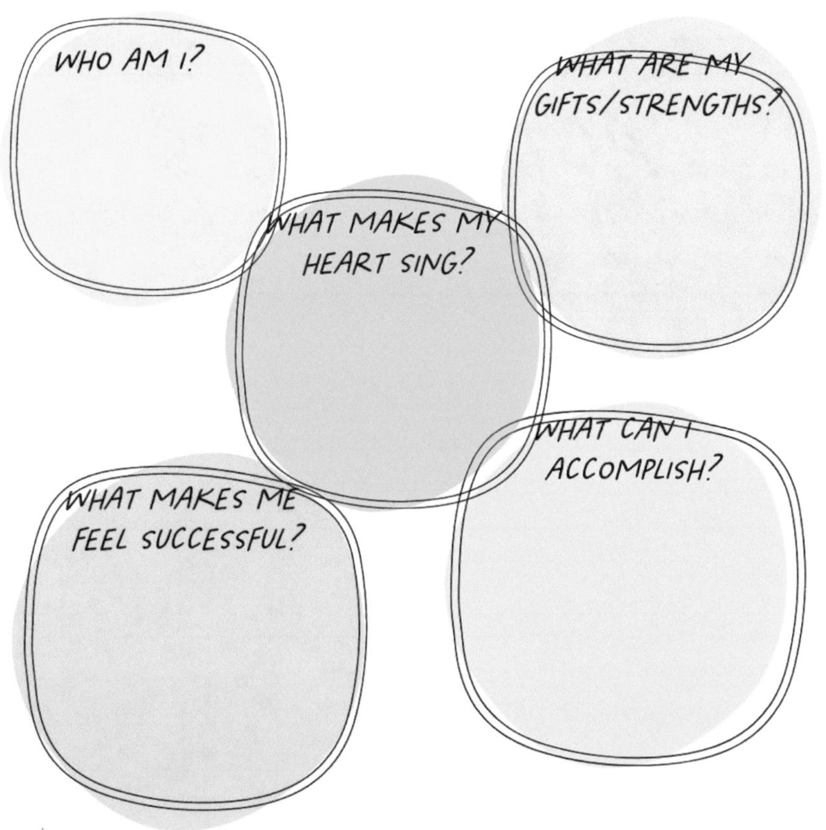
WHO AM I?
WHAT ARE MY GIFTS/STRENGTHS?
WHAT MAKES MY HEART SING?
WHAT CAN I ACCOMPLISH?
WHAT MAKES ME FEEL SUCCESSFUL?

COPYRIGHTED MATERIAL

GOAL SETTING

WHAT I WANT: LIST 1-3 THINGS. YOU CAN DUPLICATE PAST WANTS/GOALS AND MANY TIMES YOU'LL WANT TO! REMEMBER, SETTING EVEN ONE GOAL PER MONTH IS MORE THAN GOOD ENOUGH!

GOAL SETTING = POWER

MY GOALS THIS MONTH

1. ....

2. ....

3. ....

ACTION STEPS

ACTIONS I'LL TAKE: CREATE 1-5 ACTION STEPS PER GOAL THAT YOU CAN TAKE TO ACCOMPLISH YOUR OBJECTIVE.

GOAL ....

1. ....

2. ....

3. ....

4. ....

5. ....

COPYRIGHTED MATERIAL

MY THOUGHTS & DREAMS

COPYRIGHTED MATERIAL

I CAN.............

JOURNAL PAGE

COPYRIGHTED MATERIAL

COPYRIGHTED MATERIAL

JOURNAL PAGE

I WILL............

COPYRIGHTED MATERIAL

COPYRIGHTED MATERIAL

I BELIEVE............

COPYRIGHTED MATERIAL

COPYRIGHTED MATERIAL

COPYRIGHTED MATERIAL

I REALISE............

JOURNAL PAGE

COPYRIGHTED MATERIAL

DOODLE AWAY!

COPYRIGHTED MATERIAL

MONTHLY REVIEW

I'M PROUD OF MYSELF TODAY BECAUSE:

I'M GRATEFUL TO........

BECAUSE:

I'M INSPIRED BY........

BECAUSE:

I'M LEARNING MORE ABOUT ME AND MY INNER STRENGTHS. SOME THINGS COME EASILY TO ME! MY STRENGTHS ARE UNIQUE. I LIKE HOW MY INTERESTS AND MY STRENGTHS INTERMINGLE AND SUPPORT ONE ANOTHER. I NOTICE HOW THEY BOTH KEEP EXPANDING AND GETTING STRONGER

COPYRIGHTED MATERIAL

END OF MONTH CELEBRATION!

WHAT WAS FUN?

WHAT WAS HARD?

WHAT MADE ME LAUGH?

WHO DID I INCLUDE?

WHAT DID I CHANGE?

WHAT DID I LEARN?

HOW DID I GROW?

WHAT DID I ACCOMPLISH?

HOW DID I PLOW THROUGH THE HARD STUFF?

COPYRIGHTED MATERIAL

WORDSEARCH

A	S	U	C	O	F	H	T	C	A	L	M
I	B	R	A	V	E	S	E	H	P	R	I
N	P	U	X	H	T	I	C	A	V	M	N
S	E	F	N	M	O	W	G	L	R	S	D
P	A	P	A	D	R	E	A	M	Q	T	F
I	C	C	R	E	A	T	I	V	E	S	U
R	E	V	E	N	T	N	W	E	V	O	L
E	S	T	R	E	N	G	T	H	B	D	Y
D	O	E	R	K	I	N	D	N	E	S	S
E	L	I	M	S	F	R	I	E	N	D	S
L	A	U	G	H	N	Q	S	L	A	O	G

THE FIRST FOUR WORDS THAT YOU FIND INSPIRE ____________

ABUNDANT	DREAM	INSPIRED	PEACE
BRAVE	FOCUS	KINDNESS	SMILE
CALM	FRIENDS	LAUGH	STRENGTH
CREATIVE	GOALS	LOVE	VENT
DOER	HEART	MINDFUL	WISH

COPYRIGHTED MATERIAL

MORE DOODLING !

COPYRIGHTED MATERIAL

MONTH 4 STARTING DATE: ....

I AM ...., AND I SEE BEAUTY IN THE ENVIRONMENT, IN ANIMALS, IN MY FAMILY AND FRIENDS. THE TREES, GARDEN, SUNFLOWER, CAT, DOG, AND PEOPLE THAT I LOVE ARE IMPERFECTLY PERFECT. ALWAYS GOOD ENOUGH, THOUGH. WHEN I GET DOWN ON MYSELF, I TRY TO REMEMBER THAT I AM ALWAYS GOOD ENOUGH TOO. I'M HERE FOR A REASON ~ PROBABLY TO BE ME!

Think about what you want to accomplish, have happen, and how you want to feel. What is most important to you & will benefit you now and grow with you?

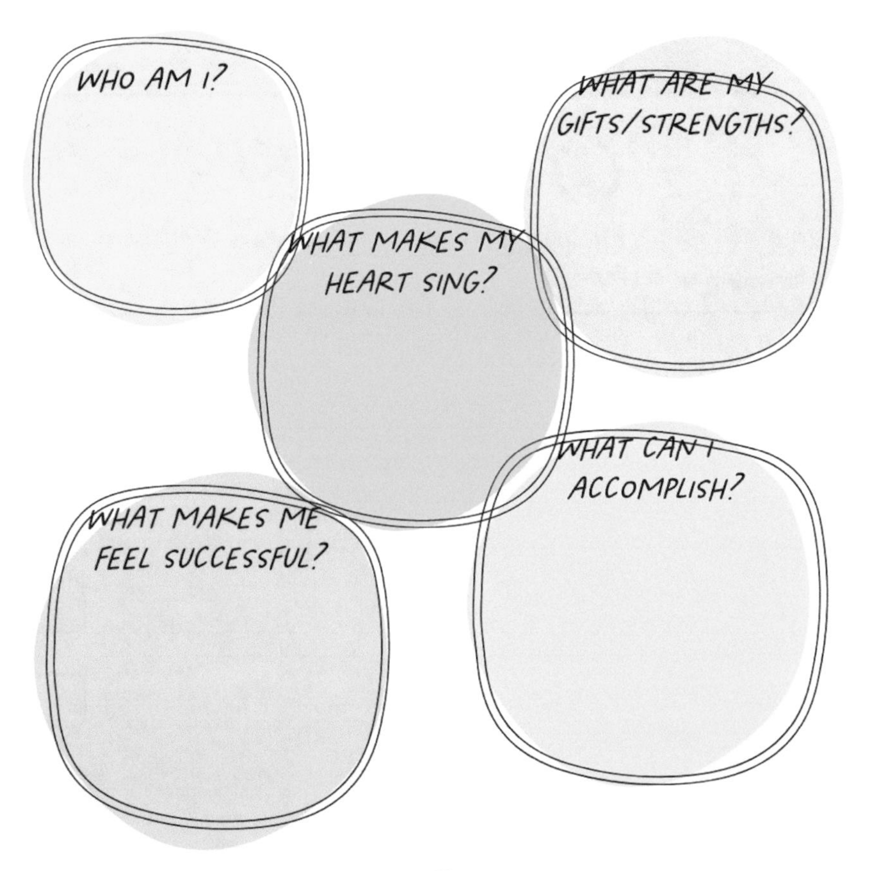
WHO AM I?
WHAT ARE MY GIFTS/STRENGTHS?
WHAT MAKES MY HEART SING?
WHAT CAN I ACCOMPLISH?
WHAT MAKES ME FEEL SUCCESSFUL?

COPYRIGHTED MATERIAL

GOAL SETTING

WHAT I WANT: LIST 1-3 THINGS. YOU CAN DUPLICATE PAST WANTS/GOALS AND MANY TIMES YOU'LL WANT TO! REMEMBER, SETTING EVEN ONE GOAL PER MONTH IS MORE THAN GOOD ENOUGH!

GOAL SETTING = POWER

MY GOALS THIS MONTH

1. ....

2. ....

3. ....

ACTION STEPS

ACTIONS I'LL TAKE: CREATE 1-5 ACTION STEPS PER GOAL THAT YOU CAN TAKE TO ACCOMPLISH YOUR OBJECTIVE.

GOAL ....

1. ....
2. ....
3. ....
4. ....
5. ....

COPYRIGHTED MATERIAL

MY THOUGHTS & DREAMS

COPYRIGHTED MATERIAL

I THINK............

COPYRIGHTED MATERIAL

JOURNAL PAGE

COPYRIGHTED MATERIAL

I LOVE............

COPYRIGHTED MATERIAL

COPYRIGHTED MATERIAL

COPYRIGHTED MATERIAL

COPYRIGHTED MATERIAL

I ENJOY............

COPYRIGHTED MATERIAL

DOODLE AWAY!

COPYRIGHTED MATERIAL

MORE DOODLING !

COPYRIGHTED MATERIAL

MONTHLY REVIEW

I'M PROUD OF MYSELF TODAY BECAUSE:

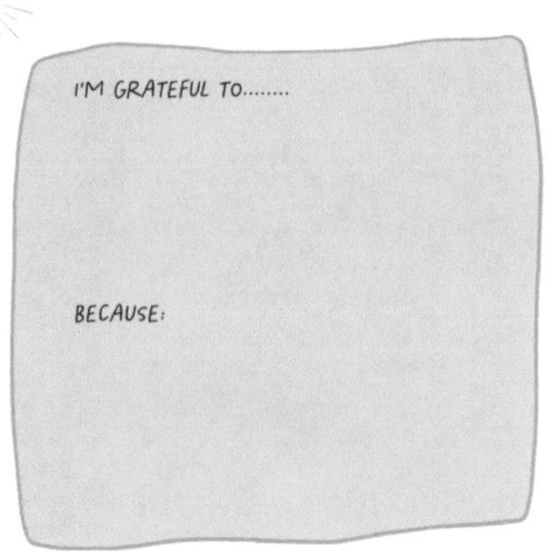

I'M GRATEFUL TO........

BECAUSE:

I'M INSPIRED BY........

BECAUSE:

I TAKE RESPONSIBILITY FOR MY ACTIONS. I APOLOGIZE QUICKLY IF I NEED TO. I LIKE CLEARING THE ENERGY. I THINK THAT'S A GOOD TRAIT TO HAVE! IT HELPS ME TO FEEL BETTER ABOUT MYSELF. I LIKE FEELING CONFIDENT TOO. BETTER THINGS HAPPEN WHEN I FEEL GOOD AND POSITIVE ABOUT MYSELF.

COPYRIGHTED MATERIAL

END OF MONTH CELEBRATION!

WHAT WAS FUN?

WHAT DID I CHANGE?

WHAT WAS HARD?

WHAT DID I LEARN?

WHAT MADE ME LAUGH?

HOW DID I GROW?

WHO DID I INCLUDE?

WHAT DID I ACCOMPLISH?

HOW DID I PLOW THROUGH THE HARD STUFF?

COPYRIGHTED MATERIAL

MONTH 5 STARTING DATE: ....

I AM ...., I CONQUER MY FEARS AND TRY NEW THINGS. I LIKE BEING A SMART RISK TAKER! I AM PROUD OF MYSELF WHEN I FACE A CHALLENGE. I HAVE GOOD DAYS AND SOME NOT-SO-GOOD DAYS - BUT THAT'S OKAY BECAUSE EACH DAY BRINGS WITH IT A NEW OPPORTUNITY FOR ME TO BE ME!

Take some time to think about the following questions & jot down any ideas that come to mind.

What are my gifts/strengths?
Who am I?
What makes my heart sing?
What can I accomplish?
ME
What makes me feel successful?

COPYRIGHTED MATERIAL

GOAL SETTING

WHAT I WANT: LIST 1-3 THINGS. YOU CAN DUPLICATE PAST WANTS/GOALS AND MANY TIMES YOU'LL WANT TO! REMEMBER, SETTING EVEN ONE GOAL PER MONTH IS MORE THAN GOOD ENOUGH!

GOAL SETTING = POWER

MY GOALS THIS MONTH

1. ....

2. ....

3. ....

ACTION STEPS

ACTIONS I'LL TAKE: CREATE 1-5 ACTION STEPS PER GOAL THAT YOU CAN TAKE TO ACCOMPLISH YOUR OBJECTIVE.

GOAL ....

1. ....

2. ....

3. ....

4. ....

5. ....

COPYRIGHTED MATERIAL

MY THOUGHTS & DREAMS

COPYRIGHTED MATERIAL

I CAN.............

JOURNAL PAGE

COPYRIGHTED MATERIAL

COPYRIGHTED MATERIAL

I WILL............

JOURNAL PAGE

COPYRIGHTED MATERIAL

COPYRIGHTED MATERIAL

I BELIEVE............

COPYRIGHTED MATERIAL

COPYRIGHTED MATERIAL

I REALISE............

COPYRIGHTED MATERIAL

DOODLE AWAY!

COPYRIGHTED MATERIAL

DOODLING MORE!

COPYRIGHTED MATERIAL

MONTHLY REVIEW

I'M PROUD OF MYSELF TODAY BECAUSE:

TA DA! I AM A MASTER RESILIENCE BUILDER.

I AM NOT AFRAID OF BEING WRONG AND MAKING A MISTAKE.
THAT IS HOW I BUILD RESILIENCE.
I DON'T TAKE MYSELF TOO SERIOUSLY.
I KEEP MY EYES ON POSITIVE ROLE MODELS THAT I RESPECT.
SOME OF MY MENTORS I KNOW PERSONALLY AND SOME I READ ABOUT.
THEY INSPIRE ME!

COPYRIGHTED MATERIAL

END OF MONTH CELEBRATION!

WHAT WAS FUN?

WHAT DID I CHANGE?

WHAT WAS HARD?

WHAT DID I LEARN?

WHAT MADE ME LAUGH?

HOW DID I GROW?

WHO DID I INCLUDE?

WHAT DID I ACCOMPLISH?

HOW DID I PLOW THROUGH THE HARD STUFF?

COPYRIGHTED MATERIAL

MONTH 6 STARTING DATE: ....

I AM ...., I'M NOTICING THAT THERE IS A RIPPLE EFFECT TO ALL THINGS. I APPRECIATE THE SMALL THINGS IN MY LIFE AS THEY MULTIPLY INTO BIGGER THINGS. I LIKE AND APPRECIATE MY FRIENDS. I AM A GOOD FRIEND AS WELL. THE HAPPIER I FEEL THE EASIER THINGS BECOME.

Think about what you want to accomplish, have happen, and how you want to feel. What is most important to you & will benefit you now and grow with you?

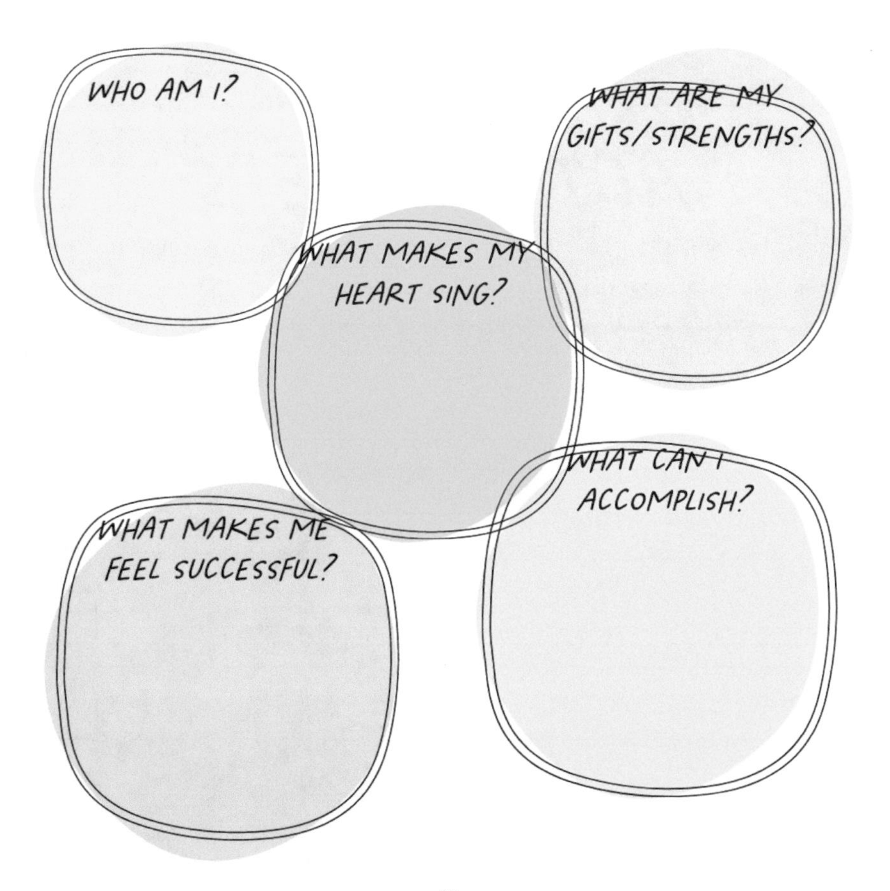
WHO AM I?
WHAT ARE MY GIFTS/STRENGTHS?
WHAT MAKES MY HEART SING?
WHAT CAN I ACCOMPLISH?
WHAT MAKES ME FEEL SUCCESSFUL?

COPYRIGHTED MATERIAL

GOAL SETTING

WHAT I WANT: LIST 1-3 THINGS. YOU CAN DUPLICATE PAST WANTS/GOALS AND MANY TIMES YOU'LL WANT TO! REMEMBER, SETTING EVEN ONE GOAL PER MONTH IS MORE THAN GOOD ENOUGH!

GOAL SETTING = POWER

MY GOALS THIS MONTH

1. ....

2. ....

3. ....

ACTION STEPS

ACTIONS I'LL TAKE: CREATE 1-5 ACTION STEPS PER GOAL THAT YOU CAN TAKE TO ACCOMPLISH YOUR OBJECTIVE.

GOAL ....

1. ....

2. ....

3. ....

4. ....

5. ....

COPYRIGHTED MATERIAL

MY THOUGHTS & DREAMS

COPYRIGHTED MATERIAL

COPYRIGHTED MATERIAL

COPYRIGHTED MATERIAL

COPYRIGHTED MATERIAL

I LOVE............

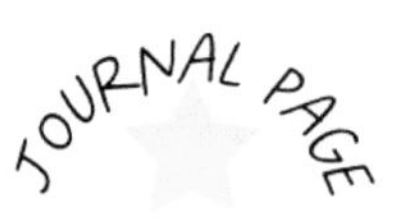

COPYRIGHTED MATERIAL

I THANK...........

COPYRIGHTED MATERIAL

I ENJOY............

COPYRIGHTED MATERIAL

DOODLE AWAY!

COPYRIGHTED MATERIAL

MONTHLY REVIEW

I'M PROUD OF MYSELF TODAY BECAUSE:

I'M GRATEFUL TO........

BECAUSE:

I'M INSPIRED BY........

BECAUSE:

I CHOOSE TO BE KIND TO MYSELF FIRST, SO THAT I CAN BE KIND TO OTHERS. I AM MY OWN BEST FRIEND! I CELEBRATE SMALL SUCCESSES AND REALIZE THAT I AM SUCCESSFUL. I CHOOSE TO WALK MY PATH WITH CREATIVITY AND PURPOSE.

COPYRIGHTED MATERIAL

END OF MONTH CELEBRATION!

WHAT WAS FUN?

WHAT DID I CHANGE?

WHAT WAS HARD?

WHAT DID I LEARN?

WHAT MADE ME LAUGH?

HOW DID I GROW?

WHO DID I INCLUDE?

WHAT DID I ACCOMPLISH?

HOW DID I PLOW THROUGH THE HARD STUFF?

COPYRIGHTED MATERIAL

WORDSEARCH

O	T	N	E	M	R	E	W	O	P	M	E
P	C	O	N	V	I	C	T	I	O	N	L
E	S	Y	T	N	A	I	L	L	I	R	B
N	T	E	N	I	U	N	E	G	N	G	A
M	R	S	Y	T	I	R	A	L	C	R	E
I	A	H	O	N	E	S	T	Y	L	A	T
N	T	N	S	T	R	I	V	E	U	T	E
D	E	T	N	G	I	F	T	E	D	E	L
E	G	S	S	E	C	C	U	S	E	F	H
D	Y	S	S	E	R	P	X	E	R	U	T
L	E	A	D	E	R	S	H	I	P	L	A

THE FIRST FOUR WORDS THAT YOU FIND INSPIRE ____________

ABLE
ATHLETE
BRILLIANT
CLARITY
CONVICTION
EMPOWERMENT
EXPRESS
GENUINE
GIFTED
GRATEFUL
HONESTY
INCLUDER
LEADERSHIP
MANNERS
OPEN MINDED
STRATEGY
STRIVE
SUCCESS

COPYRIGHTED MATERIAL

TRUSTING MY INSTINCTS IS THE ULTIMATE ACT OF TRUSTING MYSELF.

COPYRIGHTED MATERIAL

MONTH 7 STARTING DATE: ....

I AM ...., AND I AM AWARE OF MY SURROUNDINGS AND SHOW UP TO LIFE WITH GREAT ENERGY! I BELIEVE IN MYSELF. I TRUST MY INSTINCTS ABOUT PEOPLE AND SITUATIONS. TRUSTING MY INSTINCTS IS THE ULTIMATE ACT OF TRUSTING MYSELF. I KEEP MY EYES, EARS, AND THOUGHTS ON POSITIVE OUTCOMES AND MOVE IN THAT DIRECTION.

Think about what you want to accomplish, have happen, and how you want to feel. What is most important to you & will benefit you now and grow with you?

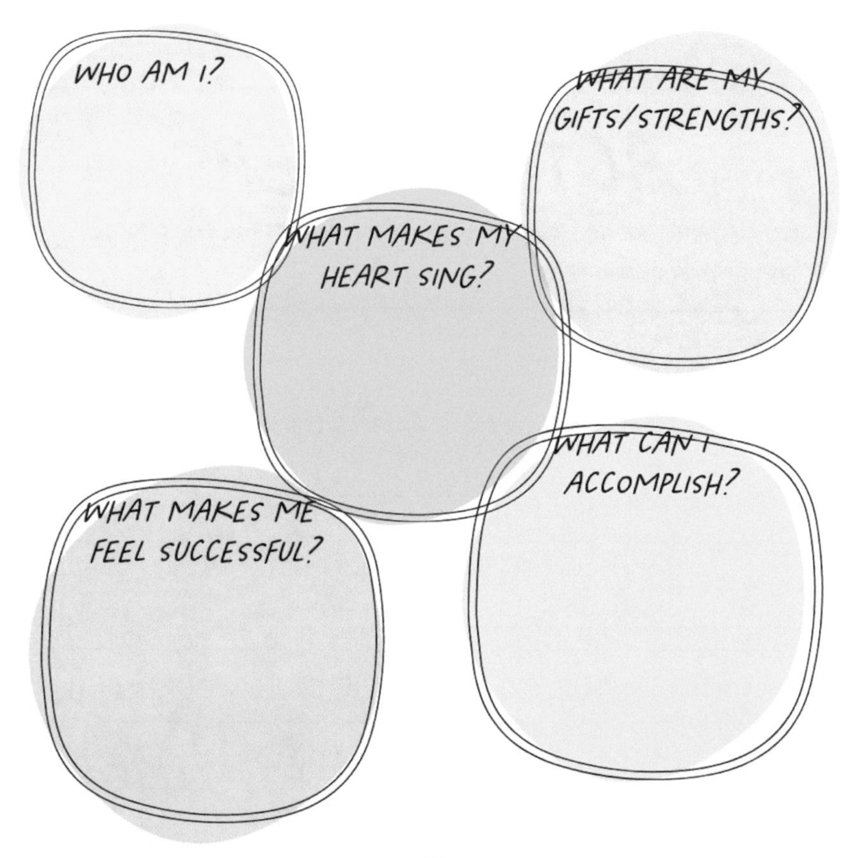
WHO AM I?
WHAT ARE MY GIFTS/STRENGTHS?
WHAT MAKES MY HEART SING?
WHAT CAN I ACCOMPLISH?
WHAT MAKES ME FEEL SUCCESSFUL?

COPYRIGHTED MATERIAL

GOAL SETTING

WHAT I WANT: LIST 1-3 THINGS. YOU CAN DUPLICATE PAST WANTS/GOALS AND MANY TIMES YOU'LL WANT TO! REMEMBER, SETTING EVEN ONE GOAL PER MONTH IS MORE THAN GOOD ENOUGH!

GOAL SETTING = POWER

MY GOALS THIS MONTH

1. ....

2. ....

3. ....

ACTION STEPS

ACTIONS I'LL TAKE: CREATE 1-5 ACTION STEPS PER GOAL THAT YOU CAN TAKE TO ACCOMPLISH YOUR OBJECTIVE.

GOAL ....

1. ....

2. ....

3. ....

4. ....

5. ....

COPYRIGHTED MATERIAL

MY THOUGHTS & DREAMS

COPYRIGHTED MATERIAL

I CAN............

JOURNAL PAGE

COPYRIGHTED MATERIAL

COPYRIGHTED MATERIAL

JOURNAL PAGE

I WILL............

COPYRIGHTED MATERIAL

COPYRIGHTED MATERIAL

I BELIEVE............

COPYRIGHTED MATERIAL

COPYRIGHTED MATERIAL

I REALISE............

JOURNAL PAGE

COPYRIGHTED MATERIAL

DOODLE AWAY!

COPYRIGHTED MATERIAL

MORE DOODLING!

COPYRIGHTED MATERIAL

MONTHLY REVIEW

I'M PROUD OF MYSELF TODAY BECAUSE:

I'M INSPIRED BY........

BECAUSE:

I MOSTLY HAVE A BLAST!

I AM CREATING MY FUTURE WHILE FOCUSING ON TODAY.

SOME OF MY DAYS ARE HARDER THAN OTHERS.

SOME DAYS I'M SICK, SAD, OR MAD AND ON THOSE DAYS, I CAN TALK OR WRITE IT OUT. I REST WHEN I NEED TO, I CHECK MY MINDSET AND REGROUP, AND THEN TOMORROW, OR EVEN NEXT WEEK I'M RARING TO GO AGAIN!

COPYRIGHTED MATERIAL

END OF MONTH CELEBRATION!

WHAT WAS FUN?

WHAT DID I CHANGE?

WHAT WAS HARD?

WHAT DID I LEARN?

WHAT MADE ME LAUGH?

HOW DID I GROW?

WHO DID I INCLUDE?

WHAT DID I ACCOMPLISH?

HOW DID I PLOW THROUGH THE HARD STUFF?

COPYRIGHTED MATERIAL

MONTH 8 STARTING DATE: ....

I AM ...., AND I LOVE A GOOD LAUGH AND A GOOD DAY. I LOOK FOR BOTH EACH DAY - I MAKE MY ENVIRONMENT A COMFORTABLE PLACE TO BE. WHEN I NEED HELP, I ASK FOR IT. I GET ANGRY AND SAD SOMETIMES LIKE WE ALL DO. BUT I DON'T STAY IN THOSE FEELINGS FOR TOO LONG. I FEEL THEM AND THEN I REST AND REGROUP. ALSO, I KNOW THAT CONFIDENT PEOPLE ASK FOR HELP.

Think about what you want to accomplish, have happen, and how you want to feel. What is most important to you & will benefit you now and grow with you?

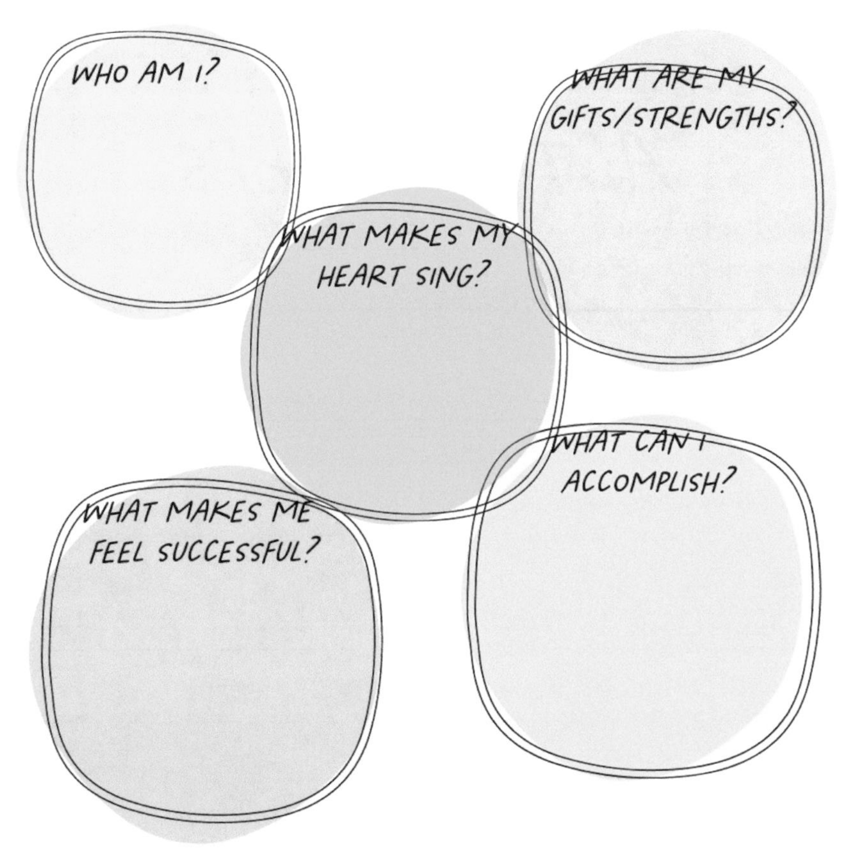
WHO AM I?
WHAT ARE MY GIFTS/STRENGTHS?
WHAT MAKES MY HEART SING?
WHAT CAN I ACCOMPLISH?
WHAT MAKES ME FEEL SUCCESSFUL?

COPYRIGHTED MATERIAL

GOAL SETTING

WHAT I WANT: LIST 1-3 THINGS. YOU CAN DUPLICATE PAST WANTS/GOALS AND MANY TIMES YOU'LL WANT TO! REMEMBER, SETTING EVEN ONE GOAL PER MONTH IS MORE THAN GOOD ENOUGH!

GOAL SETTING = POWER

MY GOALS THIS MONTH

1. .... ☐

2. .... ☐

3. .... ☐

ACTION STEPS

ACTIONS I'LL TAKE: CREATE 1-5 ACTION STEPS PER GOAL THAT YOU CAN TAKE TO ACCOMPLISH YOUR OBJECTIVE.

GOAL ....

1. .... ☐

2. .... ☐

3. .... ☐

4. .... ☐

5. .... ☐

COPYRIGHTED MATERIAL

MY THOUGHTS & DREAMS

COPYRIGHTED MATERIAL

I THINK............

COPYRIGHTED MATERIAL

JOURNAL PAGE

COPYRIGHTED MATERIAL

I LOVE.............

JOURNAL PAGE

COPYRIGHTED MATERIAL

COPYRIGHTED MATERIAL

I THANK...........

JOURNAL PAGE

COPYRIGHTED MATERIAL

COPYRIGHTED MATERIAL

I ENJOY............

JOURNAL PAGE

COPYRIGHTED MATERIAL

DOODLE AWAY!

COPYRIGHTED MATERIAL

MORE DOODLING!

COPYRIGHTED MATERIAL

MONTHLY REVIEW

I'M PROUD OF MYSELF TODAY BECAUSE:

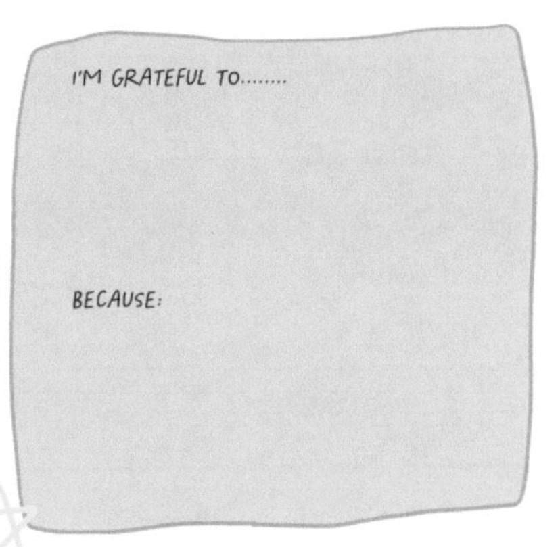

I'M GRATEFUL TO........

BECAUSE:

I'M INSPIRED BY........

BECAUSE:

THERE ARE ALL KINDS OF FAMILIES AND I LOVE MINE. I WATCH THE BABY BIRDS FLY AWAY FROM THEIR NESTS AND KNOW THAT I WILL DO THAT TOO SOMEDAY. BUT FIRST, I WILL WALK AND RUN AND LEARN AND GROW AND DREAM MY BIG DREAMS - WAY BEFORE I FLY AWAY!

COPYRIGHTED MATERIAL

END OF MONTH CELEBRATION!

WHAT WAS FUN?

WHAT DID I CHANGE?

WHAT WAS HARD?

WHAT DID I LEARN?

WHAT MADE ME LAUGH?

HOW DID I GROW?

WHO DID I INCLUDE?

WHAT DID I ACCOMPLISH?

HOW DID I PLOW THROUGH THE HARD STUFF?

COPYRIGHTED MATERIAL

MONTH 9 STARTING DATE: ....

I AM ...., AND I BELIEVE IN MY SKILLS AND ABILITIES MORE AND MORE. THE MORE I BELIEVE IN MYSELF, THE MORE I ACCOMPLISH. I LOVE BELIEVING IN MYSELF! I'M NOT PERFECT; NO ONE IS! I AM HUMAN. I AM ME ~ AWESOME, HAPPY (WELL, MOST OF THE TIME) ME!

Think about what you want to accomplish, have happen, and how you want to feel. What is most important to you & will benefit you now and grow with you?

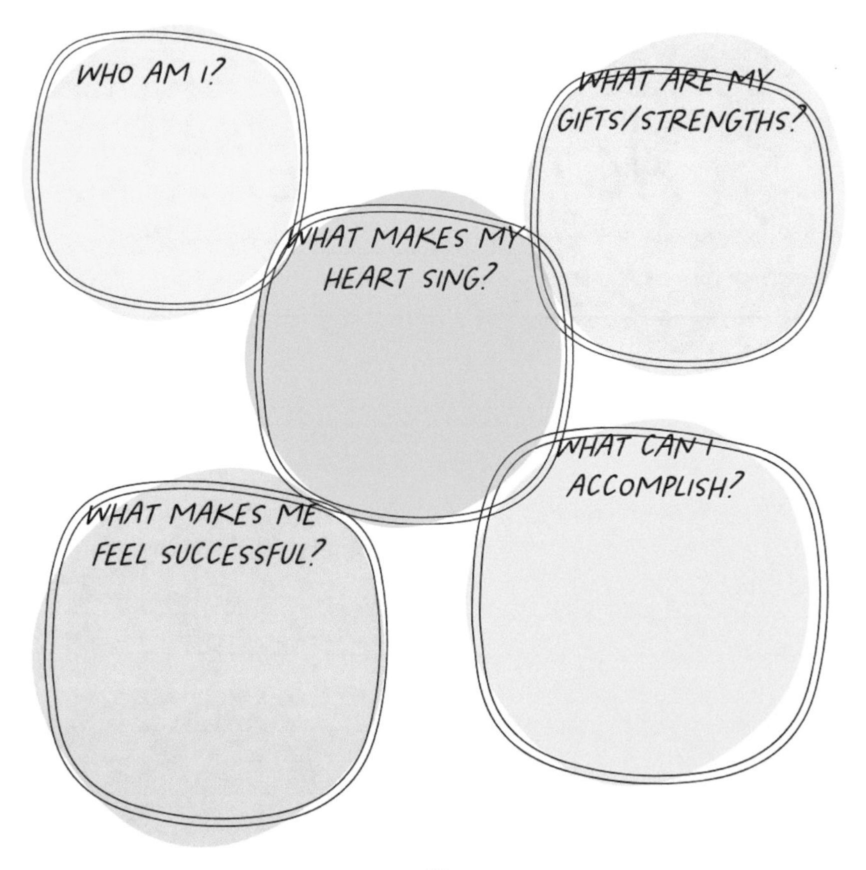
WHO AM I?
WHAT ARE MY GIFTS/STRENGTHS?
WHAT MAKES MY HEART SING?
WHAT CAN I ACCOMPLISH?
WHAT MAKES ME FEEL SUCCESSFUL?

COPYRIGHTED MATERIAL

GOAL SETTING

WHAT I WANT: LIST 1-3 THINGS. YOU CAN DUPLICATE PAST WANTS/GOALS AND MANY TIMES YOU'LL WANT TO! REMEMBER, SETTING EVEN ONE GOAL PER MONTH IS MORE THAN GOOD ENOUGH!

GOAL SETTING = POWER

MY GOALS THIS MONTH

1. .... ☐

2. .... ☐

3. .... ☐

ACTION STEPS

ACTIONS I'LL TAKE: CREATE 1-5 ACTION STEPS PER GOAL THAT YOU CAN TAKE TO ACCOMPLISH YOUR OBJECTIVE.

GOAL ....

1. .... ☐

2. .... ☐

3. .... ☐

4. .... ☐

5. .... ☐

COPYRIGHTED MATERIAL

MY THOUGHTS & DREAMS

COPYRIGHTED MATERIAL

I CAN............

JOURNAL PAGE

COPYRIGHTED MATERIAL

COPYRIGHTED MATERIAL

I WILL............

JOURNAL PAGE

COPYRIGHTED MATERIAL

I BELIEVE............

COPYRIGHTED MATERIAL

COPYRIGHTED MATERIAL

I REALISE............

JOURNAL PAGE

COPYRIGHTED MATERIAL

DOODLE AWAY!

COPYRIGHTED MATERIAL

MONTHLY REVIEW

I'M INSPIRED BY........

BECAUSE:

MISTAKES HAVE BECOME MY FRIENDS. EACH ONE THAT I MAKE GIVES ME KNOWLEDGE THAT I CAN USE TO OVERCOME MY CHALLENGES NEXT TIME AROUND. MY GOALS CREATE MY ROAD MAP - BELIEF AND JOY CREATE MY ENERGY TO ALWAYS TRY AGAIN.

COPYRIGHTED MATERIAL

END OF MONTH CELEBRATION!

WHAT WAS FUN?

WHAT DID I CHANGE?

WHAT WAS HARD?

WHAT DID I LEARN?

WHAT MADE ME LAUGH?

HOW DID I GROW?

WHO DID I INCLUDE?

WHAT DID I ACCOMPLISH?

HOW DID I PLOW THROUGH THE HARD STUFF?

COPYRIGHTED MATERIAL

WORDSEARCH

A	E	X	C	I	T	E	M	E	N	T	A
B	W	R	E	M	O	S	D	N	A	H	P
E	P	S	P	T	H	I	N	K	E	R	P
A	S	E	O	M	R	E	D	N	O	W	R
U	U	L	S	M	A	G	I	C	A	L	E
T	O	F	I	S	E	N	E	R	G	Y	C
I	R	L	T	P	T	N	W	E	V	O	I
F	E	O	I	A	H	T	L	A	E	W	A
U	N	V	V	R	I	B	R	I	G	H	T
L	E	E	E	K	E	L	Z	Z	A	D	E
L	G	C	O	M	M	U	N	I	T	Y	G

THE FIRST FOUR WORDS THAT YOU FIND INSPIRE ____________

APPRECIATE
AWESOME
BEAUTIFUL
BRIGHT
COMMUNITY
DAZZLE
ENERGY
EXCITEMENT
GENEROUS
HANDSOME
MAGICAL
POSITIVE
SELF LOVE
SPARK
THINKER
WEALTH
WONDER

COPYRIGHTED MATERIAL

MORE DOODLING !

COPYRIGHTED MATERIAL

MONTH 10 STARTING DATE: ....

I AM ...., AND I AM A CREATIVE THINKER AND A PERSON THAT CAN SOLVE PROBLEMS. I LIKE THAT I AM A CONSCIOUS THINKER AND THAT I DO NOT ACT IMPULSIVELY ~ UNLESS I AM PLAYING A SPORT AND MY AWESOME REFLEXES KICK IN! THEN I JUST GO FOR IT!

Think about what you want to accomplish, have happen, and how you want to feel. What is most important to you & will benefit you now and grow with you?

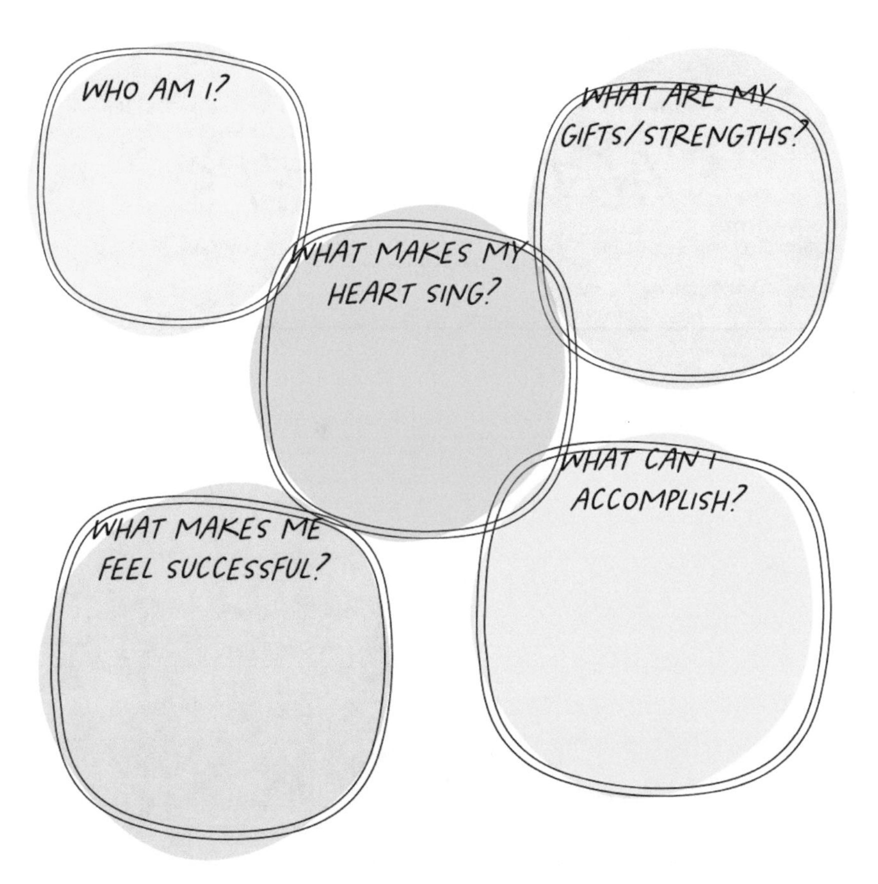
WHO AM I?
WHAT ARE MY GIFTS/STRENGTHS?
WHAT MAKES MY HEART SING?
WHAT CAN I ACCOMPLISH?
WHAT MAKES ME FEEL SUCCESSFUL?

COPYRIGHTED MATERIAL

GOAL SETTING

WHAT I WANT: LIST 1-3 THINGS. YOU CAN DUPLICATE PAST WANTS/GOALS AND MANY TIMES YOU'LL WANT TO! REMEMBER, SETTING EVEN ONE GOAL PER MONTH IS MORE THAN GOOD ENOUGH!

GOAL SETTING = POWER

MY GOALS THIS MONTH

1. .... ☐

2. .... ☐

3. .... ☐

ACTION STEPS

ACTIONS I'LL TAKE: CREATE 1-5 ACTION STEPS PER GOAL THAT YOU CAN TAKE TO ACCOMPLISH YOUR OBJECTIVE.

GOAL ....

1. .... ☐

2. .... ☐

3. .... ☐

4. .... ☐

5. .... ☐

COPYRIGHTED MATERIAL

MY THOUGHTS & DREAMS

COPYRIGHTED MATERIAL

JOURNAL PAGE

I THINK............

COPYRIGHTED MATERIAL

COPYRIGHTED MATERIAL

I LOVE............

COPYRIGHTED MATERIAL

COPYRIGHTED MATERIAL

I THANK..........

COPYRIGHTED MATERIAL

COPYRIGHTED MATERIAL

I ENJOY............

JOURNAL PAGE

COPYRIGHTED MATERIAL

DOODLE AWAY!

COPYRIGHTED MATERIAL

MORE DOODLING!

COPYRIGHTED MATERIAL

MONTHLY REVIEW

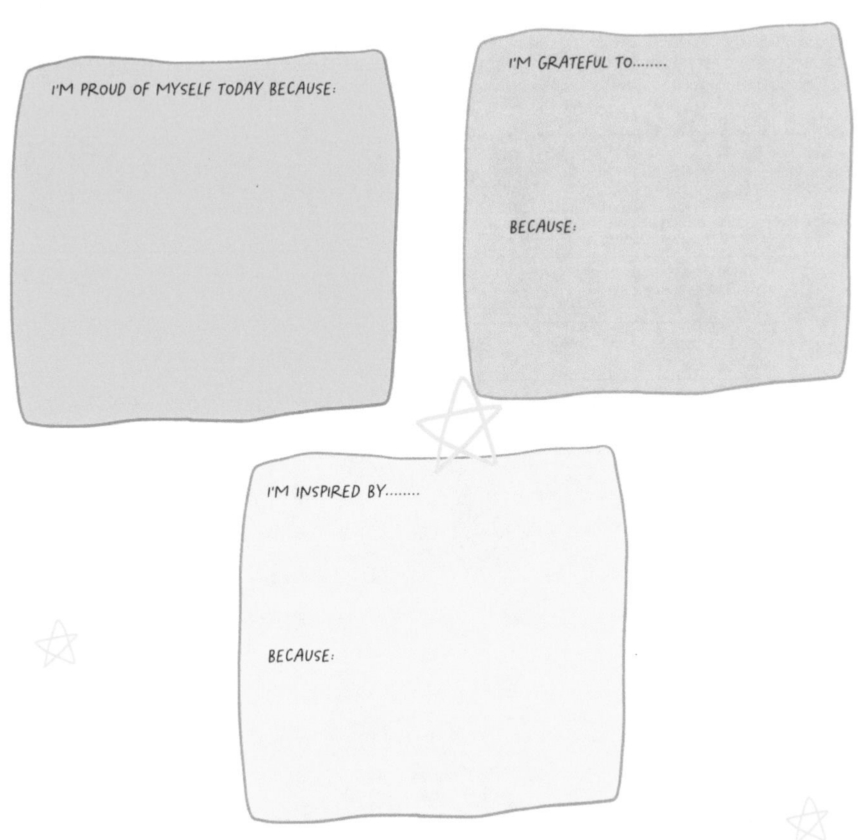

KNOWING WHAT I WANT HAS BECOME A PURPOSEFUL ACT. WHAT I WANT ARE THINGS THAT INTEREST ME; THINGS THAT I LIKE. I FEEL PULLED TO LEARN MORE ABOUT MY INTERESTS. THEY WILL BECOME MY STRENGTHS AND GIFTS THAT I WANT TO SHARE WITH OTHERS.

COPYRIGHTED MATERIAL

END OF MONTH CELEBRATION!

WHAT WAS FUN?

WHAT WAS HARD?

WHAT MADE ME LAUGH?

WHO DID I INCLUDE?

WHAT DID I CHANGE?

WHAT DID I LEARN?

HOW DID I GROW?

WHAT DID I ACCOMPLISH?

HOW DID I PLOW THROUGH THE HARD STUFF?

COPYRIGHTED MATERIAL

MONTH 11 STARTING DATE: ....

I AM ...., AND I AM EXPLODING WITH EXCITEMENT ABOUT MY ABILITIES TO LEARN AND EXPRESS MYSELF. MY THOUGHTS AND VOICE MATTER, AND I MAKE A DIFFERENCE. I STAND STRONG AND KIND AND WILL DO MY PART. I AM A DOER AND THINKER!

Think about what you want to accomplish, have happen, and how you want to feel. What is most important to you & will benefit you now and grow with you?

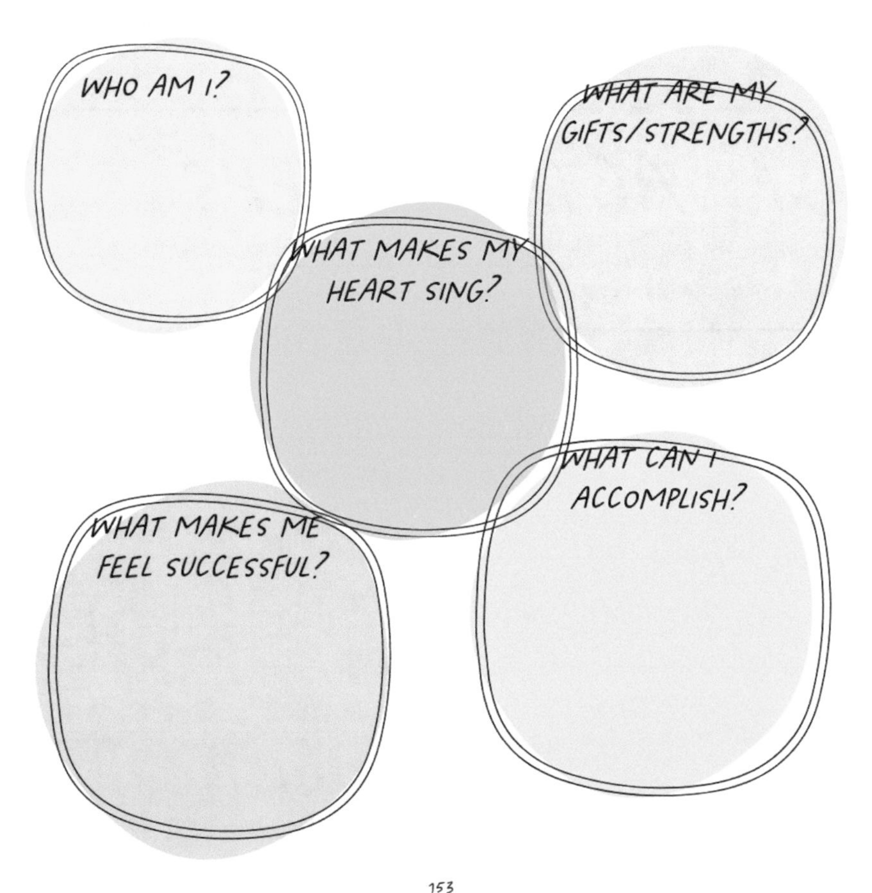
WHO AM I?
WHAT ARE MY GIFTS/STRENGTHS?
WHAT MAKES MY HEART SING?
WHAT CAN I ACCOMPLISH?
WHAT MAKES ME FEEL SUCCESSFUL?

COPYRIGHTED MATERIAL

GOAL SETTING

WHAT I WANT: LIST 1-3 THINGS. YOU CAN DUPLICATE PAST WANTS/GOALS AND MANY TIMES YOU'LL WANT TO! REMEMBER, SETTING EVEN ONE GOAL PER MONTH IS MORE THAN GOOD ENOUGH!

GOAL SETTING = POWER

MY GOALS THIS MONTH

1. .... ☐

2. .... ☐

3. .... ☐

ACTION STEPS

ACTIONS I'LL TAKE: CREATE 1-5 ACTION STEPS PER GOAL THAT YOU CAN TAKE TO ACCOMPLISH YOUR OBJECTIVE.

GOAL ....

1. .... ☐

2. .... ☐

3. .... ☐

4. .... ☐

5. .... ☐

COPYRIGHTED MATERIAL

MY THOUGHTS & DREAMS

COPYRIGHTED MATERIAL

I CAN............

JOURNAL PAGE

COPYRIGHTED MATERIAL

COPYRIGHTED MATERIAL

I WILL............

JOURNAL PAGE

COPYRIGHTED MATERIAL

COPYRIGHTED MATERIAL

I BELIEVE.............

COPYRIGHTED MATERIAL

I REALISE............

JOURNAL PAGE

COPYRIGHTED MATERIAL

DOODLE AWAY!

COPYRIGHTED MATERIAL

MONTHLY REVIEW

I'M PROUD OF MYSELF TODAY BECAUSE:

I'M GRATEFUL TO........

BECAUSE:

I'M INSPIRED BY........

BECAUSE:

I LOVE BEING PART OF A FAMILY, TEAM, OR GROUP. I LIKE THE FEELING OF BELONGING AND BEING CONNECTED. WE ALL HAVE GIFTS TO CONTRIBUTE, AND THEY ARE ALL SPECIAL, I FEEL HAPPIEST WHEN I CAN SHARE MY STRENGTHS!

COPYRIGHTED MATERIAL

END OF MONTH CELEBRATION!

WHAT WAS FUN?

WHAT WAS HARD?

WHAT MADE ME LAUGH?

WHO DID I INCLUDE?

WHAT DID I CHANGE?

WHAT DID I LEARN?

HOW DID I GROW?

WHAT DID I ACCOMPLISH?

HOW DID I PLOW THROUGH THE HARD STUFF?

COPYRIGHTED MATERIAL

MONTH 12 STARTING DATE: ....

I GROW MORE MINDFUL AND AWARE EVERY DAY. IT IS EXCITING TO BE ME - I FEEL SO ALIVE. I CAN DANCE, RUN, SING, LAUGH, LEARN, LOVE, REST, CRY, FALL, GET UP, AND THEN KEEP ON GROWING AND BEING ME. THIS HAS BEEN ONE OF THE BEST YEARS SO FAR! I DREAM BIG DREAMS! I KNOW THAT I CAN DO SO MUCH MORE. I CAN JUST FEEL IT! ADDITIONAL ACCOMPLISHMENTS WILL COME IN MY OWN TIME, MY OWN WAY, BY FOCUSING ON MY GOALS WHILE SHARING MY STRENGTHS AND MY GIFTS. I AM BEING MY BEST SELF AND THAT'S MORE THAN GOOD ENOUGH!

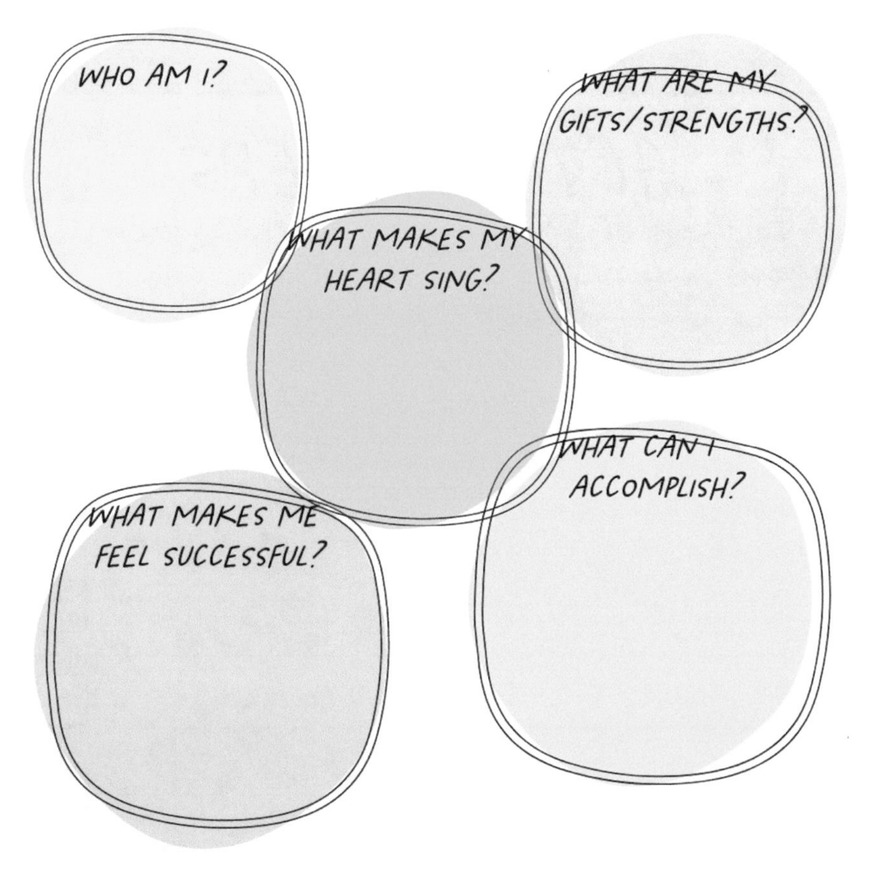
WHO AM I?
WHAT ARE MY GIFTS/STRENGTHS?
WHAT MAKES MY HEART SING?
WHAT CAN I ACCOMPLISH?
WHAT MAKES ME FEEL SUCCESSFUL?

COPYRIGHTED MATERIAL

GOAL SETTING

WHAT I WANT: LIST 1-3 THINGS. YOU CAN DUPLICATE PAST WANTS/GOALS AND MANY TIMES YOU'LL WANT TO! REMEMBER, SETTING EVEN ONE GOAL PER MONTH IS MORE THAN GOOD ENOUGH!

GOAL SETTING = POWER

MY GOALS THIS MONTH

1. ....

2. ....

3. ....

ACTION STEPS

ACTIONS I'LL TAKE: CREATE 1-5 ACTION STEPS PER GOAL THAT YOU CAN TAKE TO ACCOMPLISH YOUR OBJECTIVE.

GOAL ....

1. ....

2. ....

3. ....

4. ....

5. ....

COPYRIGHTED MATERIAL

MY THOUGHTS & DREAMS

COPYRIGHTED MATERIAL

JOURNAL PAGE

I THINK............

COPYRIGHTED MATERIAL

COPYRIGHTED MATERIAL

I LOVE............

COPYRIGHTED MATERIAL

COPYRIGHTED MATERIAL

JOURNAL PAGE

I THANK...........

COPYRIGHTED MATERIAL

I ENJOY............

JOURNAL PAGE

COPYRIGHTED MATERIAL

DOODLE AWAY!

COPYRIGHTED MATERIAL

MONTHLY REVIEW

I'M PROUD OF MYSELF TODAY BECAUSE:

I'M GRATEFUL TO........

BECAUSE:

I'M INSPIRED BY........

BECAUSE:

I AM ...., AND I HAVE ROCKED THESE LAST TWELVE MONTHS. I HAVE ALSO MADE SOME MISTAKES ~ SO I GAINED MORE KNOWLEDGE AND BECAME EVEN MORE RESILIENT. WOO-HOO! BUT MOSTLY, I SURPASSED MY GOALS. I THINK THE REASON THAT I HAD SO MUCH FUN AND SUCCESS IS BECAUSE I CONSCIOUSLY FOCUSED ON WHAT I WANTED. CONSCIOUS THINKING KEPT ME MOTIVATED AND HELPED ME TO TAKE STRATEGIC ACTION. I AM A LEADER AND TOOK THE LEAD IN MY LIFE.
I FOUND MY SPARK AND KNOW HOW TO USE IT!
I KNOW HOW TO CREATE THAT ENERGY EVERYDAY OF MY LIFE!

COPYRIGHTED MATERIAL

END OF MONTH CELEBRATION!

WHAT WAS FUN?

WHAT DID I CHANGE?

WHAT WAS HARD?

WHAT DID I LEARN?

WHAT MADE ME LAUGH?

HOW DID I GROW?

WHO DID I INCLUDE?

WHAT DID I ACCOMPLISH?

HOW DID I PLOW THROUGH THE HARD STUFF?

COPYRIGHTED MATERIAL

A	E	C	A	E	P	D	T	L	E	E	F
C	E	L	E	B	R	A	T	E	P	A	I
C	H	V	S	E	T	N	C	A	M	M	T
O	E	O	M	X	O	C	G	I	C	I	N
M	A	I	A	P	R	E	L	I	E	N	E
P	L	C	R	R	V	Y	G	V	T	D	D
L	T	E	T	E	T	A	I	E	R	S	I
I	H	T	I	S	M	H	T	H	U	E	F
S	O	L	R	S	T	N	D	N	T	T	N
H	E	R	E	F	L	E	C	T	H	D	O
B	A	U	T	H	E	N	T	I	C	O	C

THE FIRST FOUR WORDS THAT YOU FIND INSPIRE ____________

ACCOMPLISH
AUTHENTIC
BELIEVE
CELEBRATE
CONFIDENT
DANCE
EXPRESS
FEEL
FAMILY
HEALTH
MAGIC
MINDSET
REFLECT
PEACE
SMART
THRIVE
TRUTH
VOICE

COPYRIGHTED MATERIAL

MORE DOODLING !

COPYRIGHTED MATERIAL

DEAR READER:

BEFORE YOU GO AND CONQUER YOUR WORLD.......:

REMEMBER WHAT MATTERS IS THAT YOU FOLLOW YOUR VALUES, ABILITIES AND STRENGTHS. THEY CAN TAKE YOU FAR INDEED.

THEY WILL LEAD YOU IN SCHOOL, SPORTS, WITH YOUR FRIENDS, YOUR COMMUNITY, AND WITHIN YOUR FAMILY. THEY'LL KEEP EXPANDING AND CAN GIVE YOU THE COURAGE TO SHOW UP FOR YOUR LIFE.

KNOW THAT WHAT PEOPLE THINK OF YOU DOESN'T MATTER BECAUSE IT CAN'T CHANGE YOU. WHAT MATTERS IS WHAT YOU BELIEVE ABOUT YOURSELF AND THAT

YOU DO YOU.

YOU CAN BE THE KIND, POSITIVE, CONFIDENT, BRAVE ONE.

BE THAT PERSON!

IT WILL FEEL GOOD. AND YOU, WELL YOU ARE GOOD ENOUGH ALREADY.

MY VERY BEST WISHES,

Kathy

COPYRIGHTED MATERIAL

YOU
DO
YOU

COPYRIGHTED MATERIAL

Made in United States
Troutdale, OR
03/14/2024